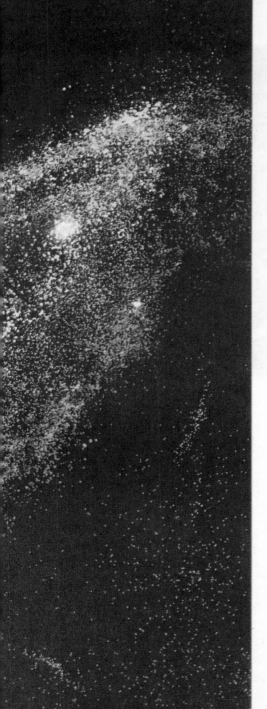

PLANETS

OTHER WORLDS OF
OUR SOLAR SYSTEM

by OTTO BINDER

Illustrated by
GEORGE SOLONEVICH

REVISED EDITION 1961

GOLDEN PRESS 🦅 NEW YORK

Library of Congress Catalog Number 61-5451

Our Family of Planets

In early times, when the Greeks looked up into the sky at night, they noticed that while most of the stars stayed in a fixed position, a few of them moved from night to night. The stars that moved were named planets, meaning "wanderers," by the ancient Greek astronomers.

However, only five such planets— Mercury, Venus, Mars, Jupiter, and Saturn—were known before the 18th century. Three more, too faint and distant to be seen with the naked eye, were discovered after the invention of the telescope. Uranus was found in 1781, Neptune in 1846, and Pluto in 1930. That makes a total of nine planets, including the Earth itself, that revolve around the central sun.

But for a long time, men believed that the Earth was the center of the universe, with the sun, planets, and all the stars whirling around our tiny world. Not until the end of the Middle Ages did brilliant men like Nicolas Copernicus (1473-1543), Johann Kepler (1571-1630), and Galileo (1564-1642) dare to say that the Earth moved and

The solar system includes 9 planets, 31 moons, many asteroids, comets, and hundreds of meteor swarms, all revolving around the sun.

the sun stayed in one place. The orbits of the planets were soon worked out when Isaac Newton (1642-1727) showed how the laws of gravitation affected the movement of the planets.

At last mankind had a clear picture of the solar system as we know it today. Mercury is the nearest planet to the sun, followed in order by Venus, Earth, Mars, Jupiter, Saturn, Uranus, Neptune, and Pluto.

Six of the planets have satellites, or moons. Mercury, Venus, and Pluto have none, while Earth has one. Mars and Neptune each have two moons; Uranus, five; Saturn, nine; and Jupiter holds the record with twelve. Thus, adding up the 9 planets and 31 moons known today, there is a community of 40 worlds, small and large, to which the Earth belongs. Several thousand asteroids, or minor planets, hundreds of comets, and countless meteor flocks complete the family of heavenly bodies that travel in orbit around the sun.

The solar system's shape is like a pancake rather than a sphere. Using Pluto's orbit as the outermost boundary, the

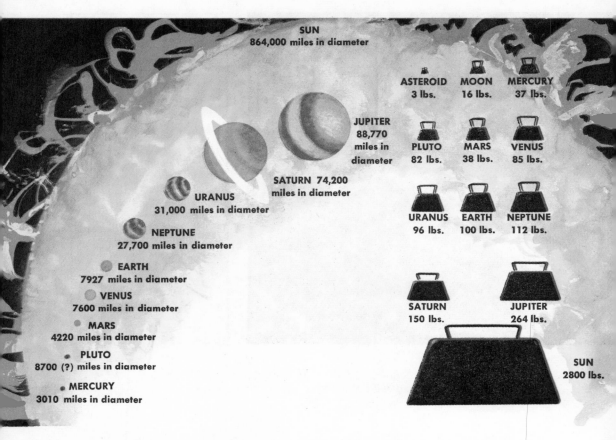

SUN
864,000 miles in diameter

JUPITER
88,770 miles in diameter

SATURN 74,200 miles in diameter

URANUS
31,000 miles in diameter

NEPTUNE
27,700 miles in diameter

EARTH
7927 miles in diameter

VENUS
7600 miles in diameter

MARS
4220 miles in diameter

PLUTO
8700 (?) miles in diameter

MERCURY
3010 miles in diameter

ASTEROID 3 lbs.

MOON 16 lbs.

MERCURY 37 lbs.

PLUTO 82 lbs.

MARS 38 lbs.

VENUS 85 lbs.

URANUS 96 lbs.

EARTH 100 lbs.

NEPTUNE 112 lbs.

SATURN 150 lbs.

JUPITER 264 lbs.

SUN 2800 lbs.

A person who weighs 100 pounds on earth would weigh 16 pounds on the moon.

solar system is almost 8 billion miles across. With very few exceptions (some comets) all the bodies circuit within that area, and also on about the same level or plane in space.

The systematic study of our planetary neighbors did not truly begin until Galileo perfected the first crude telescope in 1609. Telescopes were gradually improved as time went on, leading to the giant instruments we use today. The Hale Telescope, at Mount Palomar in California, is the world's largest, with a mirror 200 inches across. It can pick out images of stars and galaxies (groups of stars) that are vast distances away.

One new type of telescope that has recently come into use is the radio telescope. Just as optical lenses and mirrors gather visible light waves, some radio telescopes use huge, dish-shaped mirrors to reflect radio waves to an antenna. Radio signals come from all directions in space, produced by powerful electrical forces often associated with huge, churning clouds of gas between the

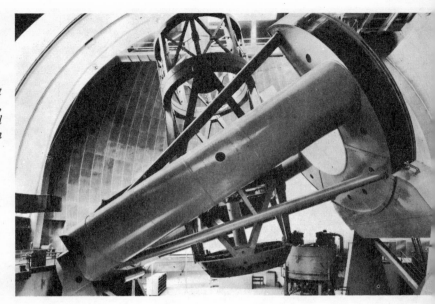

The Hale Telescope, at Mt. Palomar, California, has a 200-inch mirror and is the largest telescope in the world.

stars. Radio waves give astronomers much information that they cannot obtain with optical telescopes.

Another important instrument is the spectroscope, which analyzes light rays from space. By means of a prism or a fine grating, it splits up the ordinary white light that comes from the sun or stars into its separate wavelengths to form a rainbow of colors. The spectro-

One of the largest radio telescopes in the United States has an 84-foot antenna.

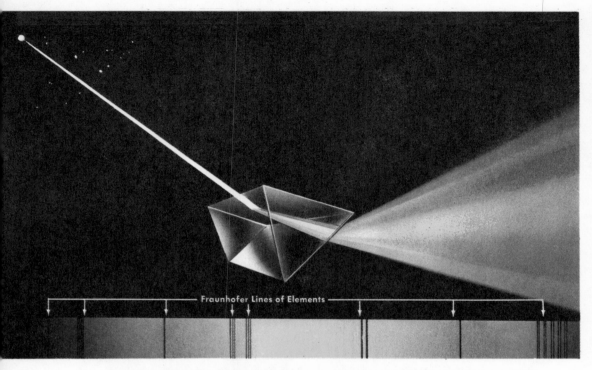

Fraunhofer Lines of Elements

The spectroscope's three-sided prism splits white light into the separate colors.

scope is also able to split certain invisible radiations such as infra-red and ultra-violet light rays.

This separation of the light radiations is a sorting-out process that reveals many facts about heavenly bodies—a planet's or a star's temperature, how fast they move through space, how fast they rotate on their axis, and (when used with other instruments) how distant they are.

A star's chemical make-up can be analyzed by the spectrograph (a spectroscope with camera attachments), for the atoms of each element—carbon, oxygen, iron, calcium, etc.—leave their "finger-prints" in the split spectrums. This is in the form of dark or light lines (Fraunhofer Lines) which occur at certain wave lengths. Each element has its own individual set of lines, different from the lines of all other elements. The spectrograph's method of chemical analysis has shown that the sun, for instance, contains at least 60 of the more than 100 elements we have on earth.

There are other astronomical instruments used for specialized purposes, but the main ones that astronomers use are the optical telescope with its attachments—the camera and the spectroscope —and the radio telescope.

10

Our Sister World

Taking off from Earth, a spaceship sent to explore the solar system could go in either of two directions—away from the sun to the outlying planets, or toward the sun where the inner planets lie. If the second flight-plan were chosen, the ship would head for Venus and Mercury, both of which are nearer to the sun than the Earth is.

Venus is our nearest neighbor, besides our moon. Every 18 months Venus is at its closest point to Earth (called the inferior conjunction), a distance of 26 million miles.

In February, 1958, radio waves were bounced off Venus and returned to Earth. Even traveling at the speed of light, 186,300 miles a second, those signals took almost 5 minutes to make the round trip.

New measurements of the solar system came to light as a result of these

Unmanned missiles like this one may some day relay information to us about Venus.

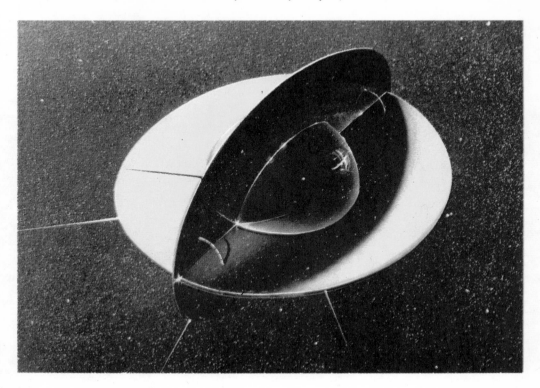

VENUS	
Volume	9/10 of earth
Average distance from sun	67,000,000 miles
Equatorial diameter	7688 miles
Period of rotation (day)	30? days
Period of revolution (year)	224.7 days
Orbital speed	21.8 miles per second
Surface gravity	0.87 of earth
Escape velocity	6.4 miles per second
Number of moons	none
Density (water=1)	5.0
Mean day temperature	over 500° F.
Mass (earth=1)	0.82
Nearest approach to earth	26,000,000 miles

Venus appears to be surrounded by clouds.

experiments. Since all radio waves travel at a fixed rate of speed through space, scientists were able for the first time to measure accurately the distances between planets and other bodies of the solar system; and these proved to be slightly smaller than had been thought.

Venus has often been called the Earth's sister world because it is approximately the same size. Its diameter of 7,688 miles is about 300 miles less than that of our planet. The density (or compactness) of Venus is 5.0 times that of water, compared to 5.5 for the Earth,

A telescopic photograph shows the markings on Venus that may be clouds.

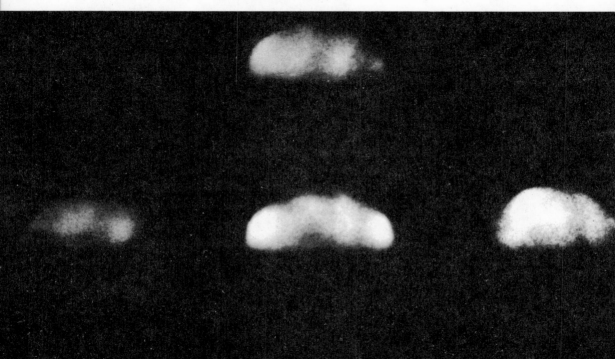

One theory suggests that Venus may be a watery world with only islands showing.

which is the most dense of all the planets. The gravity pull on the surface of Venus is about 5/6 times that of the Earth's, so that a man weighing 200 pounds on Earth would weigh only 167 pounds on Venus.

But beyond these few facts, Venus is a mystery planet to us. Its atmosphere is so dense and cloudy that our telescopes can seldom pierce through it to see what lies on the Venusian surface. We do not know if the cloudy planet is similar to the Earth or whether it is an entirely different kind of world underneath its thick blanket of mists.

We do know that Venus must have a far hotter climate than the Earth does, since it is at least 26 million miles closer to the sun. Radio telescopes have shown that the temperature on Venus is well over $500°$ Fahrenheit. (Water on the earth boils at $212°$ F.)

We don't know how much water exists on Venus. Examination of its atmosphere by the spectroscope shows just a trace of water vapor. However, only the top fringes of the air on Venus can be analyzed by our long-range instruments on the Earth. It is still possible that more water vapor exists in the lower levels. Astronomers have had several different theories about how much water, if any, the planet itself may have.

Some believe that moisture must exist because the Venusian clouds have the optical properties of earthly clouds, which are, of course, composed of water vapor. In fact, the surface of Venus may be one vast ocean from pole to pole, without any land at all except for a few islands.

Quite the opposite is the theory that Venus is a bone-dry world—one endless desert. Those who hold this theory say that the atmosphere may look so cloudy because it is filled with dust whipped up by winds from the dry Venusian plains.

But these theories must be revised when we remember what the radio astronomers have recently learned about the extremely high temperatures which exist on this planet.

Venus poses many other riddles. For one, the length of its day is not known. Ordinary photographs show only the heavy white blanket of clouds around it, and its surface markings cannot be watched to see how fast or how slowly the planet turns on its axis.

Thus, like the question of water, the ideas about Venus' rotation period also vary widely from one extreme to the other. Some astronomers believe that it always keeps one face turned toward the sun. If this is true, it would mean that Venus' day is equal to its whole year, or the length of time it takes to travel around the sun—224.7 days in earthly time.

Another theory suggests that Venus is a lifeless, hot desert world.

Ultra-violet photos, above, *and infra-red photos,* below.

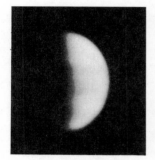

Ultra-violet and infra-red photographs show dim patches on the surface of Venus.

There is another theory, that the Venusian day is about 3 weeks long. Photographs taken with ultra-violet light, which can partially penetrate the thick clouds, show dark patches on Venus which support this latest theory. The patches are fuzzy and hard to follow but they seem to come into view at an interval of every thirty days or so, giving Venus a day about equal to our month.

Is there life on Venus? Considering the high temperature of the planet, it seems extremely unlikely that any form of life as we know it could exist. However, scientists have had many theories about this possibility, also.

Some who believe Venus is a dry desert world say it must be utterly lifeless for lack of water alone. Also, the upper atmosphere shows no trace of oxygen, the life-giving gas that we breathe on the Earth. The air of Venus seems to be mostly carbon dioxide in suffocating quantities.

Other scientists are skeptical of this, because as yet nobody knows what lies in the lower atmosphere, which is beyond the reach of our spectroscopes. They say it is possible that near the surface of Venus there lies a mixture of gases, including oxygen and water vapor. This might allow life to exist, in their view. But the high surface tempera-

While circling the sun, Venus shows different phases to the Earth just as the moon does.

ture probably means that any water is steam, so life might not exist at all.

However, all these theories are sheer guesswork. Exactly what kind of world will be known for certain only when a rocket probe spins close enough to Venus to detect surface conditions.

Seen from the Earth, Venus is the most dazzling star in the heavens. At its peak it is ten times brighter than Sirius, the most brilliant of the fixed stars, and four times as bright as Mars or Jupiter among the planets. Venus can sometimes be seen in broad daylight. And if the moon is absent on a clear night, Venus is even bright enough to cast its own shadows.

Because it circles within the Earth's orbit and because we usually see it from an angle, where it is only partially lighted by the sun, Venus shows different phases, like our moon. Venus is brightest as a crescent that covers about 35 per cent of its disk. The "full" Venus is less bright because at that time it is farthest from the Earth. At that posi-

16

tion, 160 million miles away, its disk seems six times smaller than it appears as a crescent.

Venus can never be a midnight star, for it stays too close to the sun at the angle that we see it from the Earth. Venus is in the sky for four hours at the longest, either before dawn or after sunset, so it is called either the morning star or the evening star, depending on which time of the day it is seen.

Like Mercury and Pluto, Venus has no moon. But if you were on Venus you might think there was a moon when you were looking up at the Earth through a rift in the clouds. The Earth would shine in the Venusian sky four times brighter than Venus shines for us, for the "full" Earth would appear at the closest approach of the two planets, when they were only 26 million miles apart. Even our moon would be clearly visible as a smaller body circling around the superbrilliant Earth.

An intense aurora may be the answer to one mystery about Venus, called the Ashen Light. This is a pale glow that is often seen on the unlighted portion of Venus, when telescopes show it during its crescent phase.

Venus is an evening star for 3 months and a morning star for 15 months. It is visible to us for only 4 hours, before sunrise and after sunset.

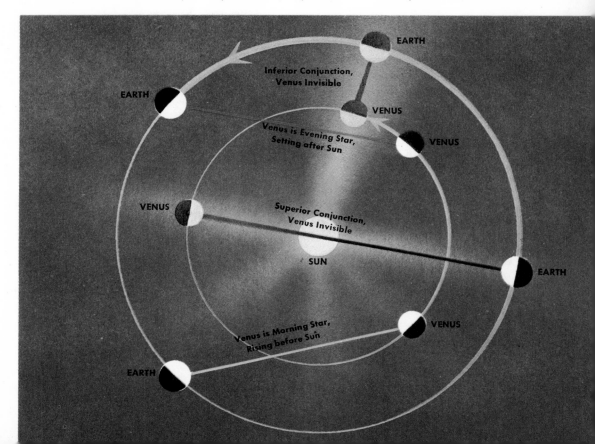

The Smallest Planet

Mercury is our second evening star, but because it never gets very far away from the sun, it can only be seen after sunset in a still-bright sky, and thus is not as well-known as Venus. It is the planet closest to the sun, circling at an average distance of 36 million miles. But its orbit is very elliptical, so that it swings within 28 million miles of the sun at its perihelion, or closest point, and recedes to 43 million miles at the aphelion, or farthest point.

The Romans gave the name of their winged god, Mercury, to this planet. It

MERCURY	
Volume	.06 times earth
Average distance from sun	36,000,000 miles
Diameter	3010 miles
Period of rotation (day)	88 days
Period of revolution (year)	88 days
Orbital speed	29.8 miles per second
Surface gravity	4/10 of earth
Escape velocity	2.6 miles per second
Number of moons	none
Density (water=1)	5.3
Mean temperature	
dayside	644° F.
nightside	−450°? F.
Mass	1/20 of earth
Nearest approach to earth	48,500,000 miles

was an apt name, for Mercury speeds faster in its orbit than any other planet. Mercury's year is also the shortest of all the planets'—its trip around the sun takes only 88 days.

The Romans, however, gave this planet *two* names, calling it Mercury as the evening star, and Apollo when it appeared as the morning star. Alternately, about every two months, Mercury is a morning and evening star. But the Romans, knowing nothing of orbits, did not suspect that Mercury and Apollo were the same star. Not until the 17th century did Kepler show with his chart of planetary orbits how Mercury dashed to opposite sides of the sun six times during an earthly year. When it is west of the sun, Mercury rises ahead of it and is called the morning star. When east of

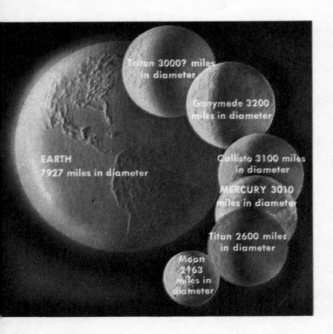

Several of the moons of other planets are larger than Mercury itself is.

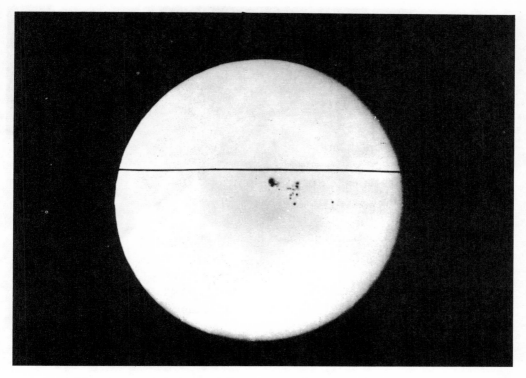

Mercury passes in front of the sun only 12 or 13 times each century.

the sun, it is the evening star, and follows the setting sun.

But we must give the Romans credit for at least seeing Mercury. Many people today have never seen it, unless they have picked exactly the right time. Although Mercury is a fairly bright star, it is never seen in the darkness of true night, but only in the pre-dawn glow or at twilight, never more than two hours before sunrise or two hours after sunset. This is because Mercury is in a very close position to the sun when viewed from the distant vantage point of Earth, and is, therefore, usually lost to sight in the brilliance of the solar glare.

Mercury is the smallest of the nine planets, having a diameter of 3,010 miles. In fact, Saturn's moon, Titan, and Jupiter's moon, Ganymede, are larger than this tiny planet. Also, the diameter of the Earth's moon is only a little less than 1,000 miles shorter than the diameter of Mercury.

Mercury turns only one face to the sun, just as the moon does to the Earth. This dayside, because of the sun's radiant nearness, receives ten times the amount of heat that the earth does. The surface temperature there is over 644 degrees, so that metals with a low melting point, such as tin and lead,

19

would exist only as molten pools or rivers.

On the other hand, the nightside of Mercury must be a frozen wasteland with a temperature close to absolute zero, 459.4 degrees below zero Fahrenheit (the point at which a substance would have no molecular motion, and therefore no heat). However, in between the dayside and nightside is the so-called twilight zone, about 200 miles wide, where temperatures would average about halfway between. Only here could spaceships from the earth land safely and avoid boiling heat or bitter cold. Mercury has little if any atmosphere and only a few dim surface markings have ever been seen on it through our telescopes.

Mercury's Dayside

Mercury's Nightside

Mercury exhibits phases as Venus does and for the same reasons. Mercury, too, is only a crescent when we see it as a morning or evening star when it is nearest to the earth. The planet is undoubtedly barren of any life on its blistering dayside or deep-frozen nightside, although there is a faint possibility of life in the twilight zone. It is unlikely that our future space explorers will find much use for Mercury, except perhaps as a convenient station from which to observe the nearby sun.

The temperature on Mercury varies over 1000 degrees between daytime and nighttime.

20

The Best-Known Planet

The Earth itself is the sixth largest planet, coming in between the three smaller and five larger worlds that are part of our solar system.

The Earth has always been known to be a round ball slightly flattened at the top and bottom, like a door knob, for its diameter from the North Pole to the South Pole is 28 miles shorter than it is through the Equator.

An additional story is told by the space satellites that circle the Earth today. The satellites react to the Earth's gravitation and as they orbit, there appear slight but surprising variations in their paths. These variations make it appear that part of the Southern Hemisphere of the Earth's surface is 25 feet farther from the Earth's center, while the same part of the Northern Hemisphere is 25 feet closer. At the same time, it appears that the South Pole is closer to, and the North Pole farther from, the center, by 50 feet.

This gives the Earth a new shape—that of a pear, in addition to the well-known door knob shape. However, this variation is so slight that the Earth would seem to be perfectly round if seen from a spaceship. The 28-mile flattening of the poles could not be noticed, much less the 25-foot bulges.

If the earth is rigidly pear-shaped, the molten interior theory may be wrong. The drawing at left, greatly exaggerated, shows the newly discovered dimensions of the earth.

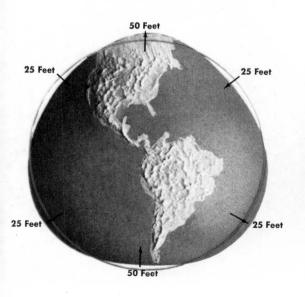

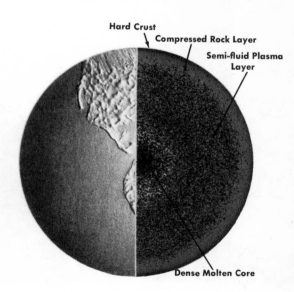

EARTH	
Diameter	
equatorial	7926 miles
polar	7898 miles
Orbital speed	18.5 miles per second
Escape velocity	6.96 miles per second
Density (water=1)	5.5
Distance from sun	
closest	91,400,000 miles
furthest	94,600,000 miles
Mass (weight)	6 thousand billion billion tons
Age	5 billion years

the Earth is in a semi-molten, plastic state; it is now believed that this interior part may be solid.

The Earth is gaining new "moons," the artificial satellites, all the time. Several are orbiting now, and many more will follow in time. Though man-made, these satellites follow the same gravitational rules that any natural moon does. They shine, just as our moon does, by reflected sunlight, and the round satellites like the Vanguard also exhibit phases.

Still, this unexpected discovery has interested the geophysicists, who study the Earth inside and out. They had formerly believed that inside the hard crust, about 30 miles thick, the rest of

A brand new discovery about our moon came late in 1958. For the first time, what appeared to be a volcanic eruption in a crater was detected and

The earth's moon is the largest satellite in proportion to its planet.

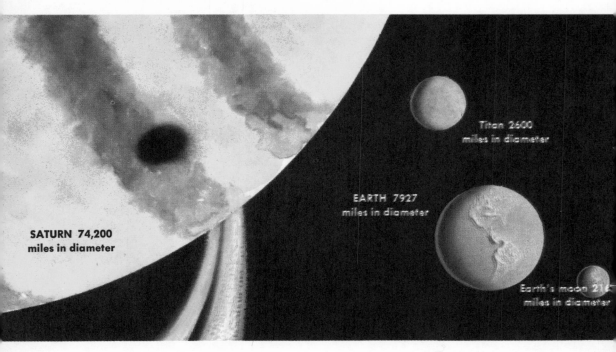

SATURN 74,200
miles in diameter

Titan 2600
miles in diameter

EARTH 7927
miles in diameter

Earth's moon 21
miles in diameter

Many earthly terms are used on moon maps, but lunar "seas" do not exist. What first appeared to be vast bodies of water were later discovered to be wide, flat plains. There are jagged mountains and steep valleys, and thousands of high-walled craters pockmark the barren surface.

Straight Wall

Copernicus Crater

Alps Mts

Mare Imbrium
(Sea of Showers)

photographed. The theory that the moon is a cold, dead world without a molten core may also have to be altered if this was a true eruption.

Our moon is the biggest of all moons in relation to its mother planet. Several moons are actually larger, such as Ganymede, which has a diameter of 3,068 miles compared to our moon's 2,160, but Ganymede is only one twenty-eighth the size of Jupiter, its mother planet, while our moon is one-fourth the Earth's size. So, proportionately, our moon is the larger one of the two.

Although it is the closest of all worlds to us, the moon is as different from the Earth as it can be. Its surface is pitted with over 30,000 known craters, some as large as 170 miles wide. Early astronomers who first observed the moon named many of its landmarks after earthly ones. But the moon mountains are bare and jagged without green forests or snow-capped peaks. The so-called "seas" are really wide, flat plains. The moon has no air or water at all.

Without air there can be no wind or sound on the moon. Without water, there can be no rain or clouds or lightning. The daytime temperature under the sun's direct rays reaches 250 degrees Fahrenheit, while at night it sinks to 112 degrees below zero. Under those harsh conditions, the moon is considered to be completely lifeless.

Since the moon always keeps one face turned toward us, we have never seen its other side. But the Russian moon-probe, Lunik III, equipped with cameras, circled the moon on October 6, 1959, and sent back radio-transmitted pictures of the other side. Soon, spaceship crews will land on the moon and see it all for themselves.

The Living Planet

Leaving Earth and heading away from the sun, our spaceship would have six planets to visit. After Venus, Mars is our nearest planetary neighbor, sometimes coming as close to the Earth as 35 million miles, as it did in 1956. As Mars is not obscured by heavy clouds, we can study it through our telescopes more closely than we can the cloud-covered Venus.

In some ways, Mars is remarkably similar to Earth. One rotation on its axis takes about 24½ hours, so its day is almost equal to Earth's. It is tipped on its axis almost as the earth is, and thus has the same four calendar seasons—spring, summer, fall, and winter. But because Mars takes 687 days to circle the sun, giving it a year almost double ours, its seasons are twice as long as they are on the Earth.

MARS	
Volume	.15 times earth
Average distance from sun	142,000,000 miles
Mean diameter	4200 miles
Period of rotation (day)	24 hours, 37 minutes, 23 seconds
Period of revolution (year)	687 days
Orbital speed	15 miles per second
Surface gravity	2/5 of earth
Escape velocity	3.1 miles per second
Number of moons	2
Density (water = 1)	3.95
Mean day temperature	39° F.
Sun's heat received	2/5 of earth
Mass (earth=1)	0.11
Nearest approach to earth	35,000,000 miles

Although it is about 50 million miles farther away from the sun than the Earth is, Mars is not much colder than the Earth. In the Martian summer the temperature at the equator can approach 80° F. In the Martian winter the thermometer drops to around 125 degrees below zero. Any life that exists on Mars must be able to withstand these intense temperature changes.

Photographs show that the polar ice cap recedes between the Martian winter and summer.

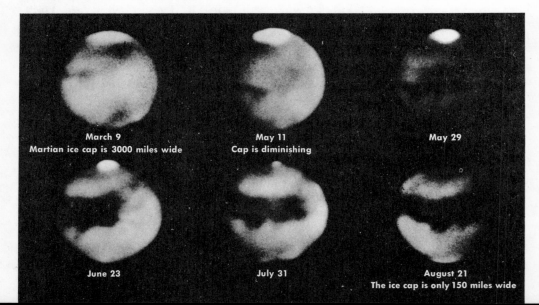

March 9
Martian ice cap is 3000 miles wide

May 11
Cap is diminishing

May 29

June 23

July 31

August 21
The ice cap is only 150 miles wide

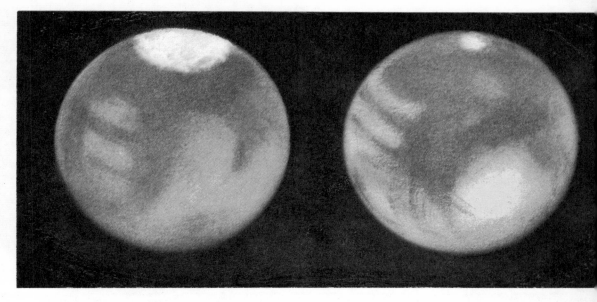

We can see that green areas on Mars expand each summer as the ice cap shrinks.

Mars' air pressure is equivalent to that of our atmosphere 60,000 feet above the Earth. Since human blood would boil at 40,000 feet above Earth, Mars would not provide a hospitable atmosphere to humans.

The air on Mars is about one tenth as dense as Earth's, and may extend 1,000 miles out from the planet. Clouds have been observed, suggesting that Mars has either dust or water vapor. The caps at the North and South Poles reflect light as Earth's icecaps do; so scientists assume that Mars' atmosphere may contain water vapor. However, the Martian ice or snow is probably just a few inches thick, unlike our giant ice caps. Still, each spring the Martian polar caps shrink, possibly forming water vapor. What appear to be clouds then seem to drift around the planet.

Besides this, each summer, large brown areas on Mars turn a definite

Primitive plant life may exist on Mars.

25

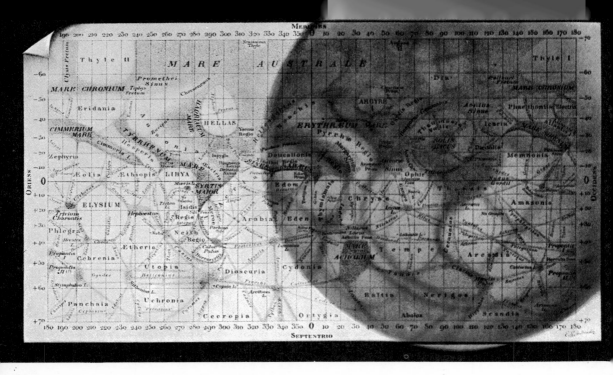

Early maps showed Mars as having seas and lakes, and a canal system that never existed.

greenish color that spreads over more and more of the planet. Many astronomers are convinced that those green patches are Martian vegetation that thrives every summer, then wilts the next winter, just as plants do on the Earth.

Some observers, however, attribute the color changes to chemical processes taking place in the Martian soil when moisture arrives. They maintain that life cannot exist on the Red Planet because only small traces of oxygen and carbon dioxide—gases that are necessary to all life on the Earth—have been found in the Martian air, which appears to be composed mainly of nitrogen and argon gases.

However, evidence seems to point toward Mars being a planet with life, even if the green growths are nothing more than primitive plants, such as lichens, algae, moss, and fungi.

Biologists have found simple forms of life existing under amazing conditions on the Earth. There are bacteria that thrive in boiling-hot springs, viruses able to withstand temperatures from freezing down to minus 200 degrees, and algae that live without oxygen and survive in the dimmest sunshine. Any of those hardy life-forms might be able to exist on Mars.

Also, the deep-sea fish and seaweeds that have been dredged up from thousands of feet down in our own oceans

26

show that life can thrive under immense pressure, with only a slight amount of oxygen, and totally without sunshine—quite the opposite of life on the Earth's surface.

Further strong evidence in favor of a living Mars came recently, when scientists of the Air Force School of Space Medicine grew bacteria in special containers that duplicated conditions on Mars: low atmospheric pressure, nitrogen-argon mixture of dry air, and great extremes in temperature. The bacteria continued to grow—and seemed to thrive in this harsh atmosphere!

But the most significant clue came in 1958 when scientists used a sensitive new spectroscope to detect the *Fraunhofer Lines of organic molecules* in the light reflected from Mars. *Organic* re-fers to life. The molecules detected by the spectroscope therefore existed in some kind of living matter. This is almost definite proof that *something* is alive on Mars. The spectroscope could not reveal just which species of life contained those organic molecules, but it most certainly ruled out lifeless rock or sand.

This Martian life may be crude plant life, or perhaps bacteria. The presence of animal life in larger forms is doubtful, except possibly for worms or insects. Fish are impossible because no bodies of water exist on Mars. Birds are equally unlikely because they would require a wingspread of dozens of yards to support them in the thin air.

But one big question has been asked over and over for many years. Did

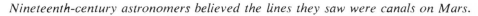

Nineteenth-century astronomers believed the lines they saw were canals on Mars.

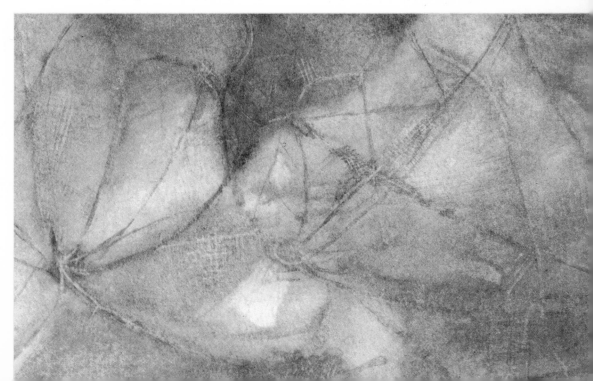

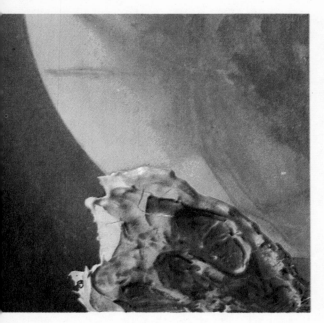

If one stood on Phobos, the nearest moon, Mars might appear like this.

higher forms of life once thrive on Mars long ago? Was there ever a civilization of intelligent beings who built a gigantic system of irrigation ditches for their crops? This theory was offered in 1877 when Schiaparelli first announced he had seen the famous "canals" on Mars through his telescope. Yet no photograph of Mars has ever clearly shown the webwork of straight lines that he and others claimed to have seen with their eyes.

Other famous astronomers, notably the Americans Percival Lowell and William Pickering, were certain that they too saw such canals and believed it possible that an ancient Martian race had built them. Lowell and Pickering

pointed out that ages ago Mars may have had big seas and a thicker atmosphere, similar to the Earth's, allowing the possibility of an earthlike evolution which might have led to the development of intelligent creatures inhabiting that planet.

Unfortunately, if it ever existed, most of the water vapor and air must have leaked into space, through long ages, because Mars' low gravity-pull could not hold them. As their seas shrank, it was theorized, the Martians strove to pump water from their polar ice caps, through a network of giant canals at least 20 miles wide. Even this failed to save their withering crops; and today, nothing is left of the dead Martian civilization except the dry canals seen in our telescopes.

This picture of ancient glory on Mars is not believed by most astronomers today. They think the "canals" are natural markings of some sort that only seem to be connected lines through an optical illusion.

The truth will be known when the first earthmen explore Mars. Perhaps unmanned missiles circling Mars with TV cameras will be able to give us the answer sooner.

When spaceships with living crews some day land on Mars, the men will find it a strange world. In the sky they will see two moons, Phobos and Deimos. The spacemen will have a total area to explore only slightly greater than the land area of the Earth, since Mars is about half our planet's size. The explorers will be able to leap great distances, for Mars' surface gravity is only two fifths of that on Earth. A man weighing 160 pounds on Earth could carry a load of 240 pounds on Mars and still weigh just 160 pounds, if he could weigh himself on that planet.

The earthmen will find Mars a quiet world. Its air is too thin to create violent storms. They will see no seas or lakes, perhaps only a few ponds and swamps. High mountains are also absent on Mars, although volcanic action, creating big clouds of yellow-red dust, has been suspected. The men would find more than half of Mars to be a smooth desert of reddish sand, which is the reason that the Red Planet appears to be that color to earthly eyes.

From Mars, Earth would appear to be a magnificent pale blue or white star, because of our planet's sparkling blue oceans and vegetation. And because its orbit is closer to the sun than Mars' is, the Earth would show different moonlike phases to the explorers standing on Mars.

The Earth observed through a telescope from Mars would exhibit moonlike phases.

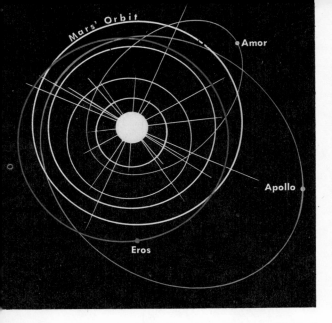

Mars' Orbit

Amor

Apollo

Eros

Many asteroids have eccentric or elliptical orbits that sometimes come close to Earth.

Second-Class Worlds

Beyond Mars, and before Jupiter, is the belt of asteroids, or minor planets. Being tiny, the asteroids are difficult to see and were not known to exist until 1801, when Ceres was discovered. It is the largest asteroid, but it is only 480 miles in diameter.

Today almost 2,000 asteroids are known. About 400 are larger than 10 miles in diameter. All the rest are tinier, being little more than mountains floating in space. Hermes and Adonis are each about a mile wide. Many still smaller asteroids may exist, perhaps as many as 50,000.

Some asteroids have misfit orbits that do not stay in the zone between Mars and Jupiter. Eros, in fact, has an orbit almost entirely within the orbit of Mars. Eros is believed to have an irregular shape like a huge brick. Almost none of the asteroids are round, as planets and moons are.

Tiny Hermes swings far inward toward the sun in its eccentric orbit and once came within a million miles of the Earth. Because of its extreme orbital eccentricity, it is doubtful whether Hermes will ever be sighted again.

The asteroids are generally thought to have originated at the same time as the solar system did.

Most of the meteoric matter from the asteroids exists in the solar system, and is held in the sun's gravitational field. Millions of meteoroids, no larger than grains of sand, strike the Earth's atmosphere day and night, to burn up from air friction, appearing as the well-known but misnamed "shooting stars." At certain times of the year, meteor showers become brilliant displays of fiery streaks throughout a whole night. Despite the tiny size of its particles, enough meteoric dust lands to increase the Earth's weight by at least 1,000 tons a day.

Larger meteorites are uncommon. Those of marble or baseball size ex-plode violently in the Earth's atmosphere and are called *bolides* (fireballs). At a few times through history, giant meteoroids too big to burn up, and traveling at speeds of nearly 30 miles per second, crashed to Earth, forming deep craters. Of a dozen or two large meteor craters known around the world, the largest is Chubb Crater in northern Quebec—11,500 feet wide and 1,300 feet deep. Some huge meteorites (as they are called when they land on Earth) have weighed at least 34 tons.

According to one theory, comets were originally part of the asteroids. This seems logical because the heads of comets have comparatively little

Halley's Comet makes a complete journey in its orbit every 76 years.

Giacobini's Comet, 1906   *Daniel's Comet, 1907*

weight (mass) and are mostly balls of glowing dust and gas. Lowell once called comets "a big bagful of nothing." When passing near planets, stars can be seen through their semi-transparent heads. If a comet struck the Earth, there would probably be a major catastrophe, but the Earth probably would not disintegrate.

Comets have been seen and recorded since ancient times. Halley's Comet, which reappears about every 76 years, was reported by the Chinese nearly 2500 years ago, in 467 B.C.

In the past, many people feared that a comet's glowing tail could poison the Earth's air. However, when the Earth passed through the tail of the Comet of 1861, and of Halley's Comet in 1910, no slightest trace of gas, poisonous or otherwise, was found in our air. This

is because the tails are really only long streaks of gas, even thinner than the airless vacuum we are able to make in scientific laboratories!

The tails of the comets, which, in spite of their name, actually precede the heads, appear only when the frozen comets from outer regions sail in to pass near the sun. The sun's heat vaporizes frozen gases in the comet's head, which then stream out for millions of miles. The record tail, 200 million miles long, was displayed by the Comet of 1843. But some comets never develop tails at all, and others have several.

Comets' heads are also huge, usually 50,000 miles wide. The giant of them all was the Holmes Comet, seen in 1892. A million miles in diameter, it was larger than the sun. Yet its gas-dust

Morehouse's Comet, 1908   *Comet Peltier*

matter probably weighed less than a mountain or island on the Earth.

More than 1,000 orbiting comets have been charted to date and many thousands more have been reported once. New ones constantly appear from outer space. Many comets have extreme orbits that swing far beyond Pluto, and they will not return for thousands of years for another visit to the area of the sun.

On the other hand, Encke's Comet, one of the short-period comets, returns regularly every 3.3 years. It was visible in February, 1961 and should be visible again in mid-1964. The short-period comets are a group of about 100 that belong chiefly to the Jupiter and Saturn families, with a few in the Uranus and Neptune families. They swing out to the orbit of one of those four planets at one end of their journey. In periods ranging from 3 to 100 years, they circle the sun at the other end of their elliptical orbits, appearing in our skies only if they happen to pass near the Earth.

About one comet per year is bright enough to be seen from the Earth with the naked eye. In 1957, however three were visible. Temple II comet should be visible in June, 1962; two others may be seen in May, 1963 and 1964.

The big observatories, however, have more important work to do than hunting down new and unpredictable comets, so this search is generally left for amateur astronomers.

Any person with a small telescope has a chance to gain immortality in astronomical records for, by custom, comets are named after the person who first discovers them.

33

The Giant Worlds

Beyond the asteroid belt, our spaceship would find Jupiter, giant of the planets, looming ahead. Jupiter has a diameter at its equator of 88,770 miles. Its polar flattening is very great, so that its north and south diameter is almost 6,000 miles less. Jupiter's rotation is so fast—a day being less than 10 hours—that its equator is bulged out by centrifugal force.

This swift axial spin shortens Jupiter's day and night to just 5 hours each. A person on its equator would be whirled around at 28,000 miles per hour, as compared to 1,000 miles per hour on the Earth.

JUPITER	
Volume	1317 times earth
Average distance from sun	484,000,000 miles
Diameter	
equatorial	88,770 miles
polar	82,800 miles
Period of rotation (day)	9 hours, 55 minutes
Period of revolution (year)	11.86 years
Orbital speed	8.1 miles per second
Surface gravity (average)	2.64 of earth's
Escape velocity	38 miles per second
Number of moons	12
Density (water=1)	1.33
Mean temperature	−202° F.
Mass (earth=1)	318
Nearest approach to earth	364,000,000 miles

On Earth, the *weight* and *mass* of an object are identical. As the object moves out into space, its *weight* lessens as the pull of gravity decreases; but the mass, density, and volume remain the same. Jupiter's mass is 318 times greater than Earth's. Its surface area is about 150 times as big as our world's. The distance around its equator is 278,000 miles, farther than from the Earth to the moon.

Jupiter's average temperature is 202 degrees below zero. It orbits 5 times as far from the sun as does the Earth, and receives one twenty-fifth of the light and heat we do, per square inch.

Jupiter's atmosphere is extremely dense, but it is entirely different from the air we breathe. The atmosphere

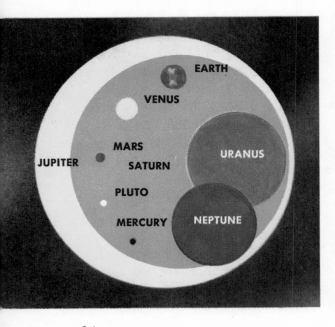

Jupiter, the largest planet, has a surface area 150 times as big as the Earth's.

JUPITER'S MOONS		
	Diameter Miles	Distance from Jupiter
AMALTHEA (J-V)	100	112,500
Io (J-I)	2060	262,100
EUROPA (J-II)	1790	417,200
GANYMEDE (J-III)	3068	666,000
CALLISTO (J-IV)	2906	1,170,000
J-VI	75	7,146,000
J-VII	25	7,300,000
J-X	10	7,300,000
J-XII	10	13,000,000?
J-XI	15	14,000,000
J-VIII	25	14,600,000
J-IX	15	14,700,000

pounds there and would hardly be able to crawl along the ground.

Through telescopes, Jupiter is a striking sight, displaying a series of yellow-brown bands, parallel to the equator, that are separate zones of the atmosphere and rotate at different speeds. The slower zones near the two poles take six minutes longer to complete one revolution than does the speedy equatorial zone.

A mysterious feature of Jupiter is the Great Red Spot, first detected in 1878. It seems to be a separate blob of heavy crimson gases which lags considerably behind the normal rotation. Bright red at first, the spot faded to pinkish-gray by 1890, but has brightened at times since then.

The radio telescope first picked up signals from Jupiter in 1955. They may be caused by violent electrical storms and lightning bolts that are nearly one

contains such poisonous or suffocating gases as hydrogen, ammonia, and methane—all noxious to humans.

Still more inhospitable to human visitors would be Jupiter's great surface gravity, which is 2.64 times the Earth's. A 100-pound boy would weigh 264

Jupiter's system of atmospheric belts can be seen clearly through a telescope.

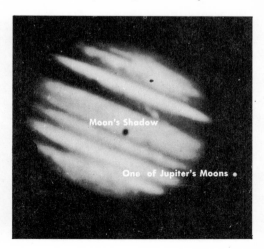

35

Seen from Amalthea, its closest moon, Jupiter would cover one fourth of the sky.

billion times more powerful than any that occur on the Earth.

Jupiter is not only the largest of all planets but has the most moons, a round dozen. Four of them—Ganymede, Callisto, Io, and Europa—are over 1,700 miles in diameter; two are bigger than our moon. All others are very small and have no names, only numbers, except for Amalthea, the closest moon. Viewed from Amalthea, only 112,500 miles from Jupiter, the huge belted planet would cover one fourth of the sky.

Moon J-VIII (in order of discovery, not distance) was known as the "lost moon" for many years. A tiny body about 25 miles in diameter, it was discovered in 1908 and was last seen in 1942, when it mysteriously became lost from view. It was rediscovered by the Mt. Wilson Observatory in 1955. An electronic computer found J-VIII in a different position, for its orbit had changed. This was not surprising as it can be the most remote of Jupiter's moons, sometimes swinging 20 million miles away. At that distance, even the

SATURN	
Volume	762 times earth
Average distance from sun	888,000,000 miles
Diameter	
equatorial	75,060 miles
polar	67,900 miles
Period of rotation (day)	10 hours, 38 minutes
Period of revolution (year)	29.5 years
Orbital speed	6 miles per second
Surface gravity	1.14 times earth's
Escape velocity	23 miles per second
Number of moons	9
Density (water=1)	0.7
Mean day temperature	—223° F.
Mass (earth=1)	95.
Nearest approach to earth	740,000,000 miles

speed another 400 million miles outward to reach Saturn, which orbits 888 million miles from the sun. Here, the sun would appear as a tiny disk one-ninetieth the size we see from the Earth. Obviously, Saturn is even darker and colder than Jupiter, with an average daytime temperature of minus 223 degrees. Its frigid atmosphere is also a poisonous brew of such gases as methane, and others in which earthly life cannot exist.

Second only to Jupiter in size, Saturn is even flatter at the poles, measuring 7,000 miles less that way than around its equator. Despite its giant bulk, Saturn outweighs the Earth barely 95 times, because it has a low density, less than that of water. Jupiter and Saturn, along with Uranus and Nep-

gravitation of Saturn, or perhaps, the sun, could pull it out of line. It is possible that still more moons of Jupiter will be found, since the planet's gravitational field is so powerful.

From Jupiter, our spaceship must

Saturn's rings, probably originating from a disintegrated moon that swung too close to the planet, are made of dust, stone, and ice particles.

Crepe Ring—11,000 miles

Ring "B"—18,000 miles

Ring "A"—width 11,000 miles

Total Width of Rings—172,600 miles

Cassini's Division—2200 miles

Distance from Crepe Ring to Saturn—6000 miles

tune, are called the liquid giants, while the Earth and smaller planets are the solid dwarfs. Saturn is probably composed of gases in a semi-fluid state, and only its innermost core could be solid. Because of its light mass, Saturn exerts such a low gravity pull that 100 Earth-pounds would increase to only 117 pounds there. Its density is so small that the planet could actually float on the surface of water.

The breathtaking beauty of its rings in telescopic views has earned Saturn the name, Gem of the Heavens. A guess as to the origin of the rings is that they may have appeared long ago after a moon swung too close to Saturn and was ripped to shreds by gravitational strains. Though the rings extend on a flat plane for almost 175,000 miles, they are no more than 25 miles thick. They are composed of countless trillions of tiny rocks and ice crystals of the exploded moon, whirling in unison around

During its year, 29½ "Earth years" long, Saturn displays its rings edgewise to earthly eyes.

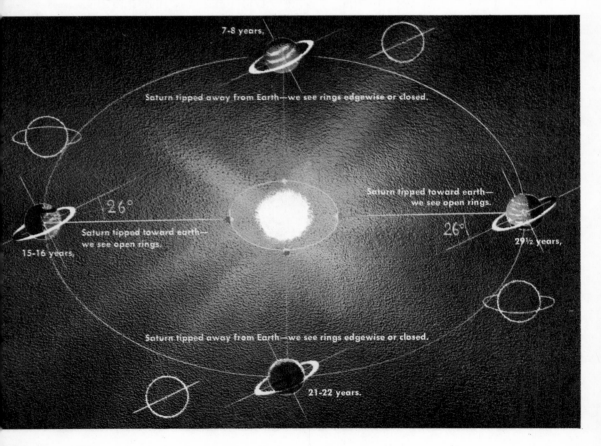

7-8 years,

Saturn tipped away from Earth—we see rings edgewise or closed.

26°

Saturn tipped toward earth— we see open rings.

Saturn tipped toward earth— we see open rings.

26°

15-16 years,

29½ years,

Saturn tipped away from Earth—we see rings edgewise or closed.

21-22 years.

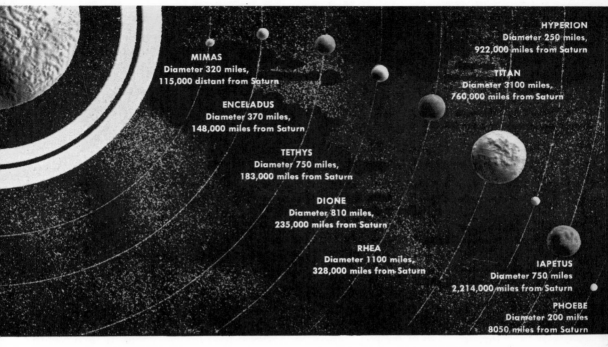

Titan is more than twice the size of any of Saturn's other eight moons.

Saturn. Stars are seen beyond and through the rings, so they cannot be made of solid material.

Since Saturn takes 29½ Earth years to circle the sun, the rings are seen edgewise from Earth every 14 to 15 years, gradually becoming almost invisible. Then, 7 or 8 years later, as Saturn is tilted differently in another part of its orbit, we are able to see the rings at their broadest width.

Close behind Jupiter in number of moons, Saturn has nine. Most of them are larger than Jupiter's, with none smaller than 200 miles in diameter. Titan is one of the largest moons in the solar system; its diameter is 3,100

miles, and it is the only one known to hold an atmosphere. It also may be the only moon to rotate independently on its axis and show all sides to Saturn. All other moons in the solar system show only one face to their mother planets, as our moon does to the Earth.

Phoebe, Saturn's outermost moon, is peculiar in that it revolves in a retrograde, or backward, direction. It is one of a handful of bodies in the solar system that orbit in a clockwise direction, whereas the sun, planets, most moons, comets, asteroids, and meteors all orbit and revolve counter-clockwise. Four of Jupiter's moons also revolve in this retrograde direction.

	URANUS	NEPTUNE	PLUTO
Volume	50 times earth	42 times earth	1.3? of earth
Distance from sun	1,786,000,000 miles	2,794,000,000 miles	3,670,000,000 miles
Equatorial diameter	29,700 miles	27,700 miles	9000 miles ?
Rotation (day)	10.8 hours	16 hours	?
Revolution (year)	84 years	165 years	248 years
Surface gravity	9/10 of earth	1.53 of earth	?
Number of moons	5	2	?
Mean day temperature	—297° F.	—330° F.	—346° F.

Adopted Worlds

If our spaceship ventured beyond Saturn, we would find three planets about which very little is known, all of them being more than a billion miles from the sun. Two of them, Uranus and Neptune, are almost the same size, each being about four times the diameter of the Earth.

Because its density is extremely low, Uranus is distinctive in that its surface gravity is 10 per cent less than the Earth's. So for once, landing on one of the giant outer planets, earthmen would not feel heavier but lighter. Of Uranus' five moons, one named Miranda was discovered as late as 1948. Neptune's second of two moons, Nereid, was found in 1949.

Uranus was the first planet to be discovered by telescope, in 1781. Astronomers then noticed that its orbit was oddly distorted, as if under the gravitational pull of an unknown planet still farther out. Then there followed an amazing mental feat by two men, independently of each other—Adams of England and Leverrier of France. Each used brilliant mathematical calculations to *predict* where that outward planet should be. Both were right, but Leverrier first got an observatory to check his theory with a telescope. They quickly found the predicted planet, later named Neptune. However, Adams is today given joint credit with Leverrier for the discovery.

Neptune's orbital revolution takes 165 years, so since its discovery in

MOONS		
URANUS	Diameter (miles)	Distance
Miranda	150?	81,000
Ariel	400	119,000
Umbriel	250	166,000
Titania	620	273,000
Oberon	500	365,000
NEPTUNE		
Triton	2500?	220,000
Nereid	200?	3,700,000?

1846 it has not yet made a full trip around the sun.

The discovery of Pluto was also a masterpiece of "detective" work by Percival Lowell, who spent years calculating where a ninth planet should be, according to slight variations in the orbits of Neptune and Uranus. Lowell died and his work was carried on by Clyde Tombaugh, a young man who examined thousands of star photographs taken in the area where the un-known planet should be shining, according to Lowell's predictions. In 1930, Tombaugh announced he had found a "star" that had moved noticeably over a period of years. It wasn't a fixed star, of course, but the ninth planet, to be named Pluto.

Little is known about this dim planet over 3½ billion miles away from the sun. It may be larger than Earth and its surface must be frozen solid, being around 346 degrees below zero. From

Although Pluto crosses Neptune's orbit, there is little danger that they will ever collide.

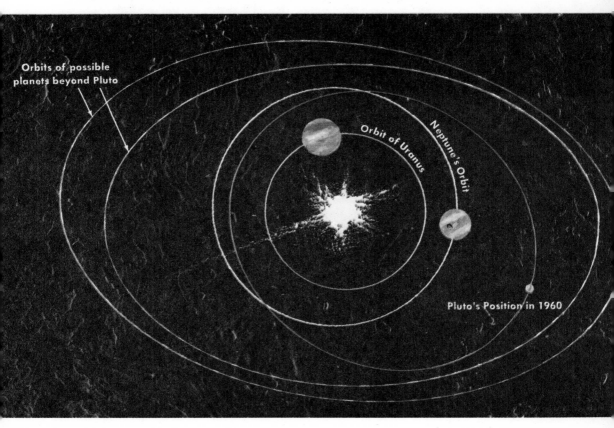

Orbits of possible planets beyond Pluto

Orbit of Uranus

Neptune's Orbit

Pluto's Position in 1960

Solar System

The Milky Way Galaxy would look like a typical spiral galaxy, seen from far off.

Pluto the sun would show only a tiny disk, hardly 250 times as bright as full moonlight.

There may be one or more planets farther out than Pluto, but it will take hard work to find them. Whatever the final boundaries of the solar system are, beyond lies the vastness of the universe.

The solar system is a tiny speck within the giant Milky Way Galaxy, which is 100,000 light-years wide (600,000 trillion miles), and holds between 100 billion and 200 billion stars, including our sun. The Milky Way, in turn, is but one galaxy out of at least one billion other galaxies tabulated by our big telescopes.

Many astronomers now believe that countless other families of planets exist in outer space. Among them would be many billions of worlds. Most would be unearthlike, but still, some of them would be almost twins of the Earth. Contrary to the old idea that Earth alone holds life, it is likely that there are a vast number of inhabited planets.

On those other earths, people much like us may be looking up at the stars in their skies and wondering if there are other thinking beings in the cosmos.

42

The Hub of the Solar System

Our spaceship has made a grand tour of the solar system. No matter where we went, or how far, we never lost sight of the sun, which is the hub of our community of worlds.

The sun is by far the largest member of the solar system, outweighing all the other bodies combined by 99 to 1. Its diameter is 864,000 miles, and if it were hollow, a million Earths could be packed into it.

As stars go, our sun is only average in both size and temperature, and is rated as a rather "cool" star. But in earthly terms, the sun is fiercely hot, having a surface temperature of 10,000 degrees Fahrenheit.

Most metals found on earth melt at around 2,000 degrees and vaporize at 5,000. Traces of vaporized metals exist in the sun, but over 90 per cent of it is composed of two gases, hydrogen and helium. These gases are compressed in the sun's core under such enormous heat and pressure — great enough to crush atoms together — that an atomic chain reaction takes place there continuously.

Thus the sun, rather than merely "burning," is somewhat like a gigantic atomic reactor, which fuses hydrogen atoms together to build up helium atoms. This is called atomic fusion, and is exactly what scientists on Earth are hoping to perfect someday as a new source of power, better than the atomic fission of uranium.

But where we intend to fuse just a few pounds of hydrogen at a time into helium, the sun uses up 600 million *tons* of hydrogen every *second*. Yet this fusion started about 5 billion years ago and can keep up for at least 10 billion more years before the sun's immense quantity of hydrogen can possibly be used up.

If Earth were placed at the sun's center, the moon's orbit would extend little more than halfway towards the sun's outer edges.

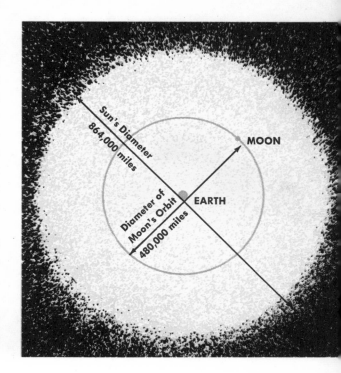

43

Any atomic process gives off a tremendous amount of energy in the form of heat, light, and other radiations. The sun's radiant energy spreads all through space and most of it is lost, except for that which strikes the planets. A tiny fraction (five billionths) of it reaches the Earth, giving us heat and light. It is also the sun's light that is reflected from the moon and other planets to make them shine.

As soon as he perfected the telescope, more than three centuries ago, Galileo discovered the sunspots. They are small black patches on the sun's surface which are cooler by 3,000 degrees than the surrounding areas. The sunspots are areas with magnetic fields.

Some giant sunspots are 90,000 miles wide, and the Earth could be dropped into them like a pebble. They are known to hurl radiations toward the Earth that cause many phenomena such as radio blackouts, brilliant displays of the aurora borealis, and disturbances at the Earth's magnetic poles that make our compass needles spin about in a wild fashion.

At the sun's core, the temperature reaches 20 million degrees F. Here hydrogen atoms are fused into helium in a continuous chain reaction, at the rate of 600 million tons per second.

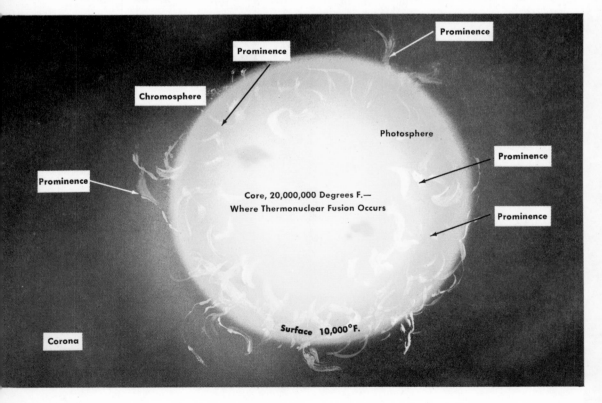

Prominence

Prominence

Chromosphere

Photosphere

Prominence

Prominence

Prominence

Core, 20,000,000 Degrees F.—
Where Thermonuclear Fusion Occurs

Surface 10,000°F.

Corona

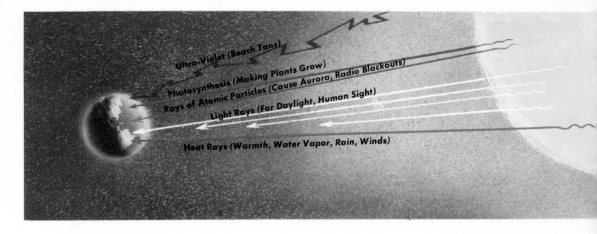

Without the sun's radiant energy, the Earth would be a cold and lifeless planet.

During the International Geophysical Year, scientists studied the sun intensively, but there are still many mysteries about the sunspots. For unknown reasons, they increase and decrease in a regular cycle of about 11 years. The last 11-year peak in 1957-58 broke all records when an average of 181 sunspots appeared each month for a year. The sunspots will diminish now, and by 1963 or thereabouts will be very rare. Then, by about 1970, the cycle will reach its peak again.

Shooting up from, or near, the sunspots at times are solar prominences. These are masses of glowing gas that are hurled out hundreds of thousands of miles into space before they sink back again. These eruptions are small in comparison to the extensions of the corona, whose streamers may even extend as far as the Earth's orbit.

Seen from the different planets, the size of the sun's disk would appear to vary greatly.

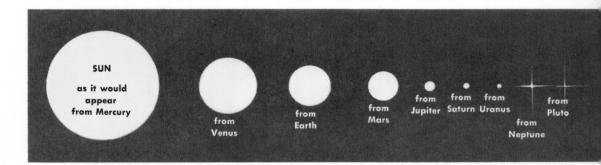

The sun's corona can be seen and studied best during a total eclipse.

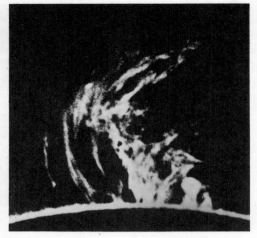

The prominences which shoot out from the sun are made of glowing gas.

During total eclipses, another feature is seen when the moon covers the blinding disk of the sun. Then the soft glow of the corona stands out, surrounding the sun as a shimmering halo of pale colors. The corona is the sun's rarefied outer atmosphere.

When and how was the solar system formed? There are several theories, some of which agree on one point—that long ago the sun had no planets and whirled through space alone.

Then, according to one concept, some passing star grazed the sun and knocked off flaming balls of matter which later cooled to become the planets and moons.

Another idea was that the sun was originally one of a pair of double stars

(binary stars) circling each other. For some reason the other star exploded. Most of its matter was hurled into outer space forever, but a few bits were caught in the sun's gravitational field, forming the planets.

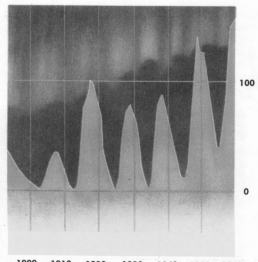

Sunspots are known to reach their peak of occurrence every 6 to 13 years.

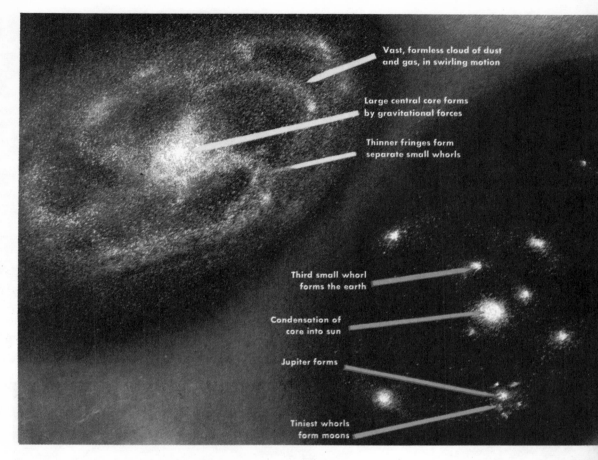

Vast, formless cloud of dust
and gas, in swirling motion

Large central core forms
by gravitational forces

Thinner fringes form
separate small whorls

Third small whorl
forms the earth

Condensation of
core into sun

Jupiter forms

Tiniest whorls
form moons

Condensing clouds of gaseous dust may have formed the sun, planets, and moon.

But neither of those theories explains where the sun itself came from in the first place. There have been numerous ideas about this. The latest theory suggests that there was at first a giant cloud of dust and gases whirling in space, in the form of a disk. Gradually, the particles in the center of the disk condensed to form a solid body, the sun, in a cold state, until increasing pressures heated it all up into incandescence. Meanwhile, the space cloud's outer fringes formed separate little whirlpools circulating around the sun nucleus. These small whirlpools later condensed into the planets and moons.

Astronomers are still divided over these and other theories. Whatever the truth is, it was at least five billion years ago, according to most estimates, that the solar system and our Earth began to be formed.

Exploring New Worlds

Early in 1959, two new planets were added to the solar system. They were the Russian moon-probe Lunik (or Mechta) and America's Pioneer IV. Both these lunar missiles missed their mark and sailed on past the moon, to take up orbits around the sun, just like the other 9 planets. The Lunik's "year" (one revolution around the sun) will be 15 months. Pioneer IV's year will be 13 months.

Other messenger rockets aimed at planets will undoubtedly get lost and become man-made planets, but that is not their real purpose. The successful missiles will eventually circle other worlds, or land on them by automatic controls. In either case, they will send back valuable information about the other planets, by means of telemetering, or radio coding.

All of these preliminary moon shots are being made in preparation for manned flights to the planets. Landings on the moon will be made first, followed by trips to Venus and Mars. Later, men will make journeys to Jupiter and, perhaps, the other remote worlds.

Lunar probes that miss the moon fly out into space to become tiny solar "planets."

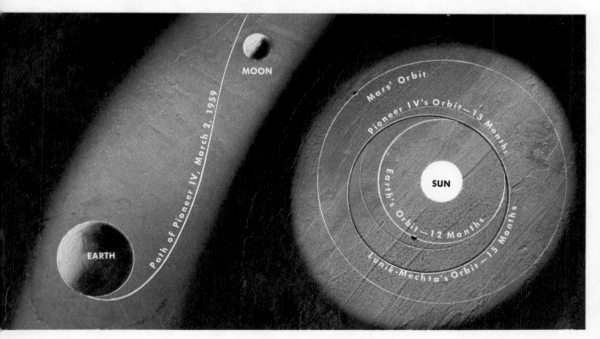

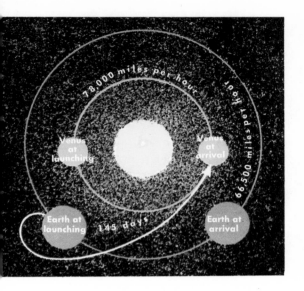

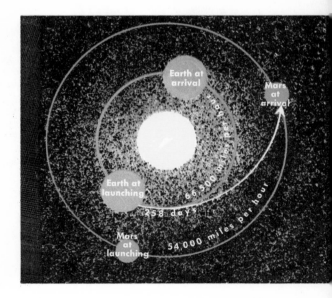

A typical path of a Venus missile.

In the case of the moon, the ship must get within 23,000 miles in order to stay within the lunar gravity field. Also, it must slow down or it will sail past, as Lunik and Pioneer IV did.

The moon trip will take about 2½ days and could be considerably shorter with a higher starting speed. But when ships leave for the nearest planets, Venus and Mars, it will take much longer — 145 days to Venus and 258 days to Mars.

In any case, the same general path will be followed by the spaceship on its way to the nearest planets. We cannot simply aim our ship straight for Venus or Mars when those planets are nearest to the Earth. Planets, including the Earth, keep moving in their orbits. At

Before this happens, men will first be trained for space flight by being sent up in orbiting satellites. Eventually, the first spaceship will reach the moon. But because of air resistance, it cannot start from the Earth's surface at the Escape Velocity of about 7 miles a second, or 25,000 miles an hour. The ship will use a slower speed to reach the thin air, 500 miles high. There, the Earth's gravity-pull is weaker, and a speed of 6.3 miles a second (22,680 miles an hour) becomes the Escape Velocity. It takes at least that much speed for any object to move far enough from the Earth to avoid being pulled back by the Earth's gravity. That point, which is about a million miles from the Earth, is where the sun's gravity would take over.

The transfer orbit of a Mars messenger.

Future interplanetary explorers will need spacesuits equipped with oxygen tanks, helmet radios, and interior air-conditioning.

starting time, Venus may be in front of the ship's nose, but by the end of the trip, months later, Venus would be many millions of miles away.

So we have to aim for where Venus *will be* when we get there. To do this, the ship itself must take up an orbital path around the sun temporarily, and become a tiny "planet." The orbit used is called a "transfer orbit" because it will cut inward from the Earth's orbit (in the case of Venus) to finally intersect Venus' orbit, 26 million miles closer to the sun.

Another problem comes up. Venus is moving 78,000 miles per hour in its orbit, while the Earth only moves 66,500 miles per hour; but the sun's gravity will whip the ship around faster in its orbit than Venus travels. That means that the ship must *slow down* or it will sail past Venus.

The trip to Mars will be different. As the ship must go farther from the sun, instead of closer, solar gravity will not accelerate the speed of the ship. And it must *speed up* to match Mars' orbital speed.

These complicated problems of astronautics (space navigation) have already been worked out fully by scientists. Once they have a ship powerful enough to use reserve rockets to speed up or slow down, they can send it to any planet for a safe landing.

Of course all spaceships going to other worlds will have to carry large food supplies for long trips, plus all the

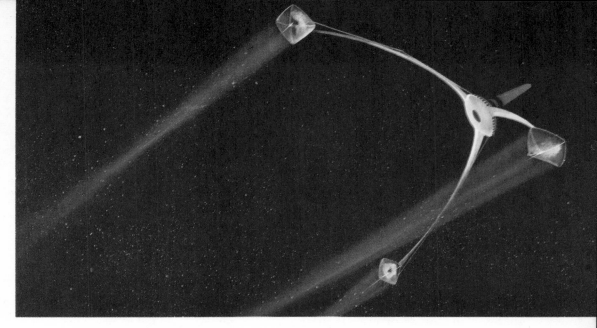

Future spaceships may attain great speeds with powerful ionic engines.

oxygen the men need for breathing, including the time they stay on a planet. Still, no matter how big the load is that the ship must carry, we will eventually have rocket engines that are powerful enough to do the job.

If our space program goes along at a rapid pace, there is little doubt that the youngsters living today will someday see the exciting headlines announcing the first man-made trips to the moon, Venus, and Mars.

Space explorers will have many new worlds to discover.

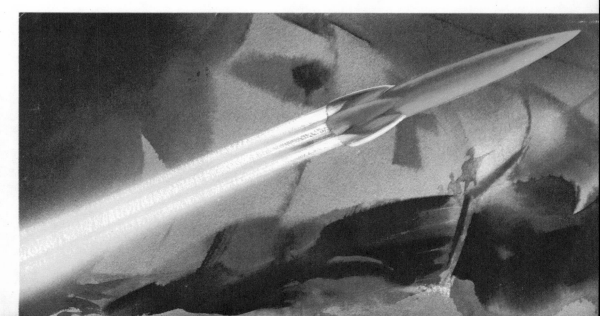

The other planets will be harder to reach because of their greater distances. The trip to Mercury won't be too difficult, as it is only 57 million miles from the earth; but the trip to Jupiter will be 390 million miles, and to Saturn, space travelers would have to go 800 million miles at the very least.

The trips to those distant planets would take several years with our present types of chemical fuel rockets. But scientists predict that atomic rockets, or another type of engine called the ionic drive, will be able to give ships speeds of hundreds or even thousands

of miles a second. This will cut the flights to the outer planets down to short months or, even, weeks.

Besides finding out many new scientific facts, will trips to other planets have any practical benefits? We do not know what we will find on other worlds, but it is certain that many discoveries will be made that we could never imagine in advance.

On the Earth, every jungle, desert, frozen tundra, or isolated island has yielded unexpected treasures when explored—medicinal herbs, precious metals, new ores, oil fields, new food prod-

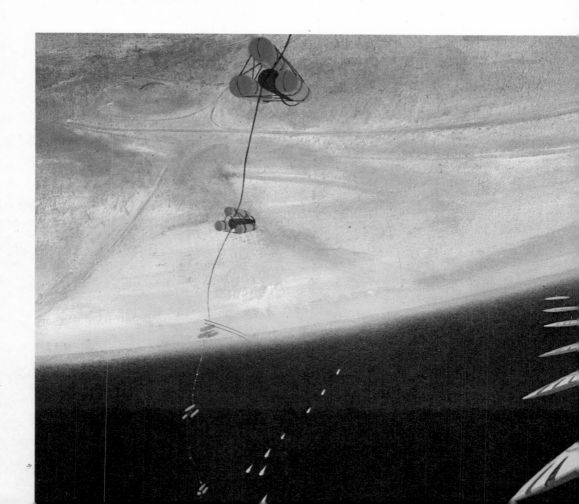

ucts, jewels—an endless list. So, every planet in space, no matter how hot, or cold, or inhospitable, may also have wonderful discoveries waiting for us, in forms unknown to us as yet. The gas, helium, was first detected in the sun by the spectroscope. This led chemists to look for it on the earth, where they found it mixed with natural gas. Helium, of course, became immensely valuable for use in balloons and blimps.

The planets can also serve as stepping-stones for the leap into outer space to visit other star-suns and solar systems. Who knows but that this might someday lead us to a twin of the Earth? This would be the crowning achievement of our great space adventure and might open up a vast new era of space commerce and trade with other inhabited planets.

In any case, exploration of our solar system can scarcely fail to advance our knowledge of the great and mysterious universe we live in; this will be the greatest reward.

Future explorers of the other planets in our solar system will someday be able to study at firsthand the unearthly wonders of the universe.

Index

PICTURE CREDITS. Mount Wilson and Palomar Observatories, pp. 9 (top), 15, 35, 46 (top). Lick Observatory, p. 23. E. C. Slipher, Lowell Observatory, p. 12, 24. Official U.S. Navy Photograph, p. 9 (bot.). Yerkes Observatory, pp. 19, 32, 33. Picture on p. 36 from *The Golden Book of Astronomy,* © 1955 by Golden Press, Inc.